SCRIBBLE YOURSELF FEMINIST

THIS BOOK IS DEDICATED
TO THE WOMAN WHO WANTS
A BETTER WORLD.

THE WOMAN WHO'S
A LOVER, A LEARNER
BUT MOST IMPORTANTLY,
A LEADER.

MAY WE ALL BECOME
OUR BEST SELVES.

PENGUIN BOOKS

UK | USA | Canada | Ireland | Australia
India | New Zealand | South Africa

Penguin Books is part of the Penguin Random House group of companies
whose addresses can be found at global.penguinrandomhouse.com.

www.penguin.co.uk www.puffin.co.uk www.ladybird.co.uk

First published 2018
001

Printed and bound in Great Britain by Clays Ltd, Elcograf S.p.A.

A CIP catalogue record for this book is available from the British Library

ISBN: 978–0–241–34773–7

All correspondence to:
Puffin Books, Penguin Random House Children's
80 Strand, London WC2R 0RL

CHIDERA EGGERUE

ILLUSTRATED BY MANJIT THAPP

PENGUIN BOOKS

Are you a feminist?

Do you believe men and women should have EQUAL rights and opportunities?

YES

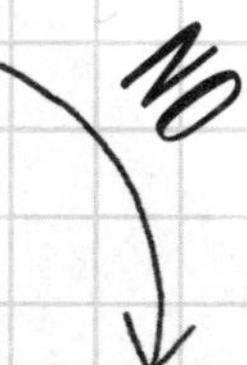

NO

You ARE a feminist

You are NOT a feminist

GOOD JOB!

And you probably suck as a person

(But it's never too late to become a better person!)

If you're still reading . . .

CONGRATULATIONS!

you're a feminist!

And welcome to

SCRIBBLE YOURSELF FEMINIST

INTRODUCTION

Ever wondered what YOU could do to make the world more equal?

Ever been told to 'MAN UP' and wanted to tear your hair out in frustration?

Ever wanted to EMPOWER yourself and the people around you?

Well guess what, you're in the right place!

Women are powerful beings. For centuries, we have been leading nations to brighter futures. It's magical to witness women break boundaries and create the change the world needs and deserves. The world literally stands NO CHANCE functioning without us!

Sadly we live in a world where women often aren't given enough of a voice.

This is where YOU come in! You have the power to change the world and you can start right now, right here. Together, we can bring about the change we want to see in the world.

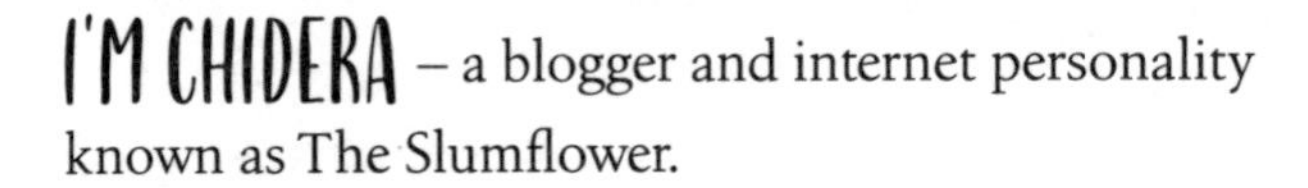

I'M CHIDERA – a blogger and internet personality known as The Slumflower.

Through social media, I have had the incredible honour of connecting with a huge audience of smart, empowered women of all ages who share my feelings. Women who want to find a way to channel their energy to bring about this change and give themselves and others a louder voice.

SCRIBBLE YOURSELF FEMINIST is an interactive journal for the engaged modern feminist. That's you!

It's FULL of activities designed to inspire, entertain and empower. And most importantly: to ENJOY.

Within these pages, you'll find lots that will encourage you to embrace and nurture your own feminist identity and hopefully make you LOL at the same time. There are mindful feminist affirmations (what I like to call my 'FEMINIST FUEL!') to keep you energized through this journey, colouring pages with some of my favourite feminist quotes and super-fun activities to get you thinking.

So get stuck in and SCRIBBLE YOURSELF FEMINIST!

LOVE, CHIDERA XX

Of course I am not worried about INTIMIDATING men. The type of man who will be intimidated by me is EXACTLY the type of man I have no interest in.

CHIMAMANDA NGOZI ADICHIE

Colour in and cut out

CHIMAMANDA NGOZI ADICHIE

is an award-winning Nigerian writer and feminist. Her influential 2012 TED talk, 'We should all be feminists', was published as an essay in 2014. She was elected to the American Academy of Arts and Sciences in 2017.

Witty Comebacks to Everyday Sexism

Sometimes, life comes at you fast. But I know you can comeback faster because you're epic and **YOU'VE GOT THIS!**

You see, the world is sometimes afraid of forward thinkers like you **BUT** fear can't stop a hero. Sexist jokes and 'banter' continue to be a part of many women's lives. Here are some perfect comebacks to make sure you have the last laugh!*

EXAMPLE: Someone honks at you from a car.

You: I am a woman NOT a traffic jam.

EXAMPLE: Idiot person makes any sexist comment.

YOU: PRETEND YOU DIDN'T HEAR AND SAY 'WHAT?' – THE MORE THEY HAVE TO REPEAT, THE SILLIER THEY SOUND.

*NOTE: Of course, there may be times that it's not safe to respond, particularly if you are on your own. In those situations, always remember your safety (rather than your brilliant sass!) should come first.

EXAMPLE: If someone tells you that you should know your place.

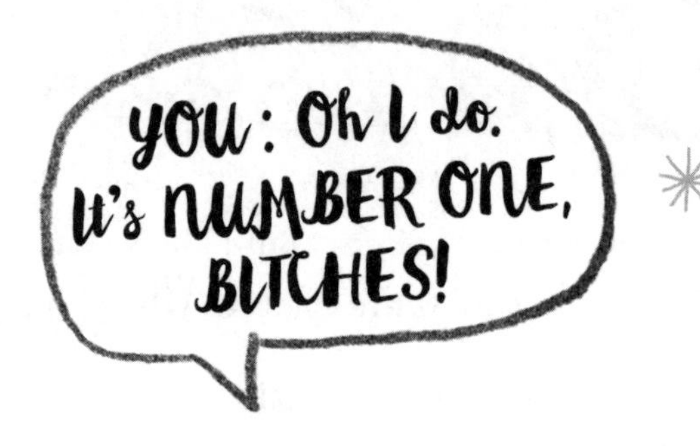

Now write some of your own:

FEMINIST FUEL

Love yourself like each day is your last.

Feminist Affirmations

Did you know that repeating daily affirmations can totally **CHANGE** the way you think? A healthy mind becomes a healthy life. Remember that your body is always listening when you speak to yourself. **BE NICE TO YOURSELF**. It's never too late to start treating your mind better!

Here's some I like to holler at myself every day:

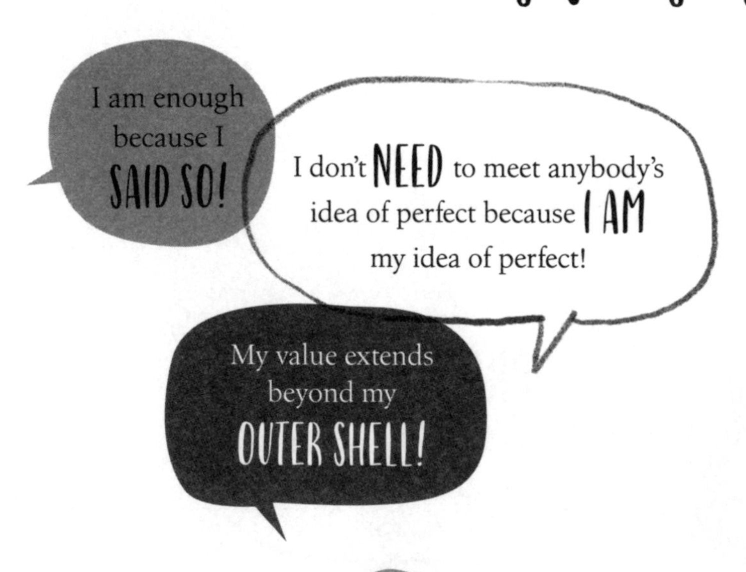

I am enough because I SAID SO!
I don't NEED to meet anybody's idea of perfect because I AM my idea of perfect!
My value extends beyond my OUTER SHELL!

You are in **ABSOLUTE CHARGE** of how you feel about yourself so why not make the daily effort to train your mind to be kind? If in doubt, ask yourself: 'Would I be friends with someone who speaks to me the way I speak to myself?' If the answer is **'NO'**, it's time for you to write some of your **OWN** affirmations to live by:

PRO TIP:

Keep your affirmations light and sparky – avoid words like 'not' and 'won't'.

IF ONE MAN CAN DESTROY EVERYTHING
WHY CAN'T ONE GIRL CHANGE IT?

Malala Yousafzai

Colour in and cut out

MALALA YOUSAFZAI

is an education activist, originally from Pakistan. She has campaigned for women and children's rights since she was a child and was awarded the Nobel Peace Prize in 2014 at the age of seventeen – making her the youngest Nobel Prize laureate.

Storytime Remix

What if Juliet decided NOT to kill herself and overcame the loss of Romeo with the help of her GAL PALS, a good therapist and some yoga classes?

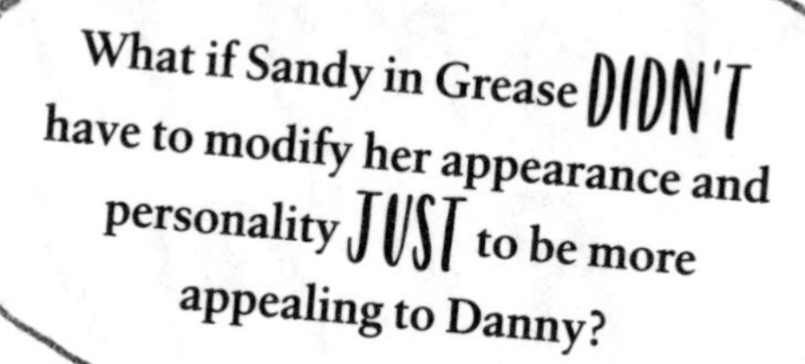

What if Sandy in Grease DIDN'T have to modify her appearance and personality JUST to be more appealing to Danny?

Life could be **VERY** different for these characters.

Let your **IMAGINATION RUN WILD** and have a go at remixing some classic stories yourself. Here's an example to get you motivated and some title suggestions to spark ideas . . .

The Little Mermaid

SEA WITCH:
Do you wanna trade your voice and legs for a prince?

THE LITTLE MERMAID:
What prince?
I came here to ask you out.

SEA WITCH:
Go on . . .

Robyn Hood and her Kick-Ass Girl Gang

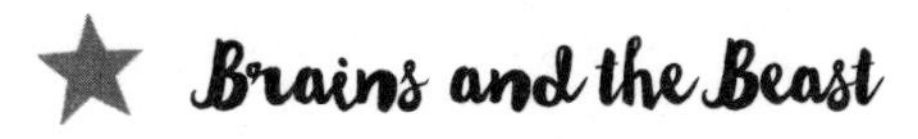

Brains and the Beast

Gay Pride (and Prejudice)

Ms Red Riding Hood – Wolf Slayer

Valentine's Day isn't just about celebrating romantic love; it's also about celebrating the people who support you all year round, especially your HOMEGIRLS!

I love to spend my Galentine's Day treating myself to some online shopping and sending my homegirls appreciation texts and tweets for all the times they've sat through my breakdowns (TRUST ME, I'VE HAD MANY).

It's time to wish them a Happy Galentine's Day in the sassiest way possible. Here are some ideas to get you started:

♥ WILL YOU BE MY GALENTINE?

♥ TALK DIRTY TO ME: 'DONALD TRUMP IS PRESIDENT'

♥ I LOVE YOU SO MUCH, I'D GIVE YOU ALL MY SOCIAL MEDIA PASSWORDS

♥ ROSES ARE RED, VIOLETS ARE BLUE, TOXIC PATRIARCHY IS DEAD AND THAT'S THANKS TO YOU!

♥ TWO GREAT THINGS ABOUT YOU:
1. YOU'RE A FEMINIST
2. ....

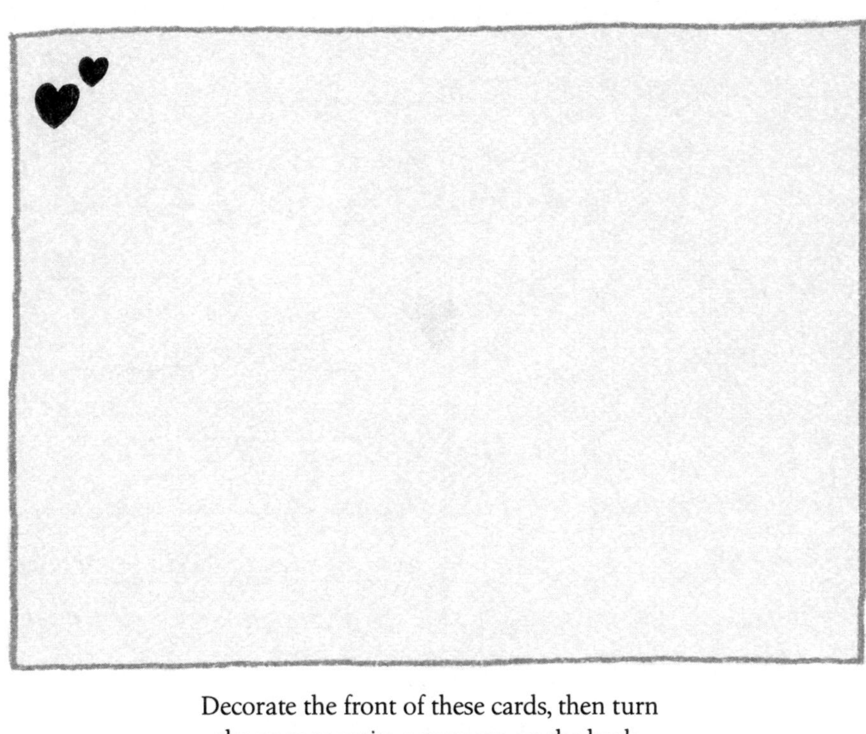

Decorate the front of these cards, then turn the page to write a message on the back.

I'M A FEMINIST. I'VE BEEN A FEMALE FOR A LONG TIME NOW.

IT'D BE STUPID TO NOT BE ON MY OWN SIDE.

MAYA ANGELOU

MAYA ANGELOU

(1928–2014) was an American writer and poet. She was also a civil rights activist and worked alongside Martin Luther King Jr. Her 1969 autobiography, *I Know Why the Caged Bird Sings*, is viewed as a landmark of African-American and feminist writing.

FEMINIST FUEL

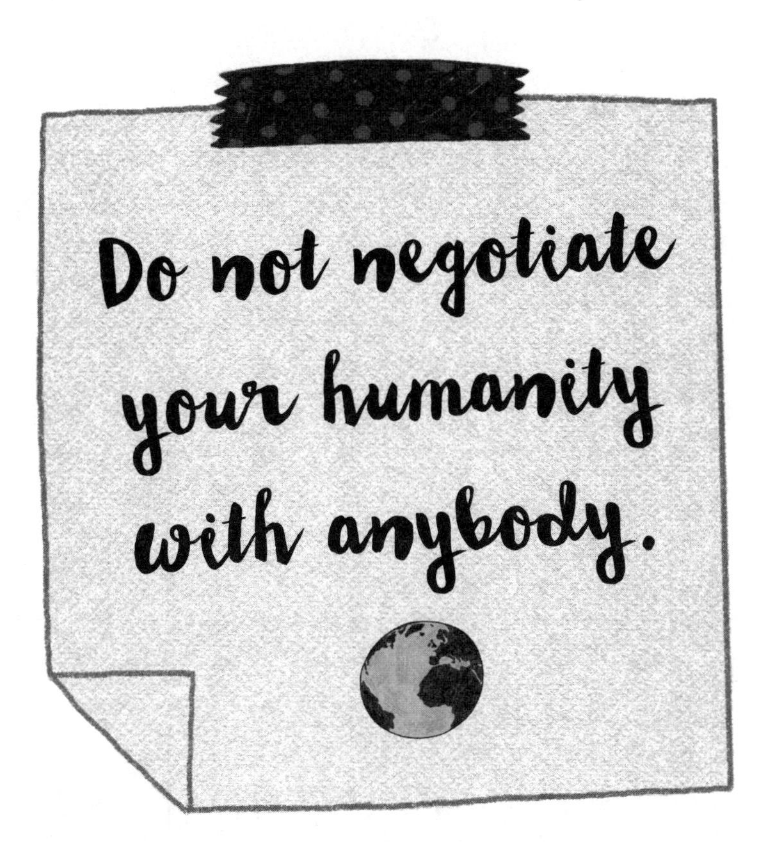
Do not negotiate
your humanity
with anybody.

FEMINIST HALL OF FAME

FEMINIST H.O.F

It's important to acknowledge our heroes. My feminist hero is my mother. WHY? Because she taught me that no matter what state I choose to show up in, I am still deserving and worthy of love. She taught me that I shouldn't ever look at myself through the male gaze because I'll only find faults in myself.

IF SHE'S NOT ICONIC, I REALLY DON'T KNOW WHO IS! WHO'S YOURS?

Here are a few total babes who have inspired me to get you started . . .

CHARLOTTE, EMILY & ANNE BRONTË

These sisters were the authors of some groundbreaking fiction during the nineteenth century. Like many female authors at the time, they originally wrote under male pseudonyms in order to get published.

IGGY POP

The 'Godfather of Punk' and a feminist, Iggy says 'I'm not ashamed to dress like a woman because I don't think it's shameful to be a woman.'

BEYONCÉ

All-round superstar babe!

KATHERINE JOHNSON

An African-American mathematician who worked at NASA and whose work was vital to the success of numerous space missions. She was honoured with the Presidential Medal of Freedom in 2015.

Now fill in the rest with your favourite feminist heroes!

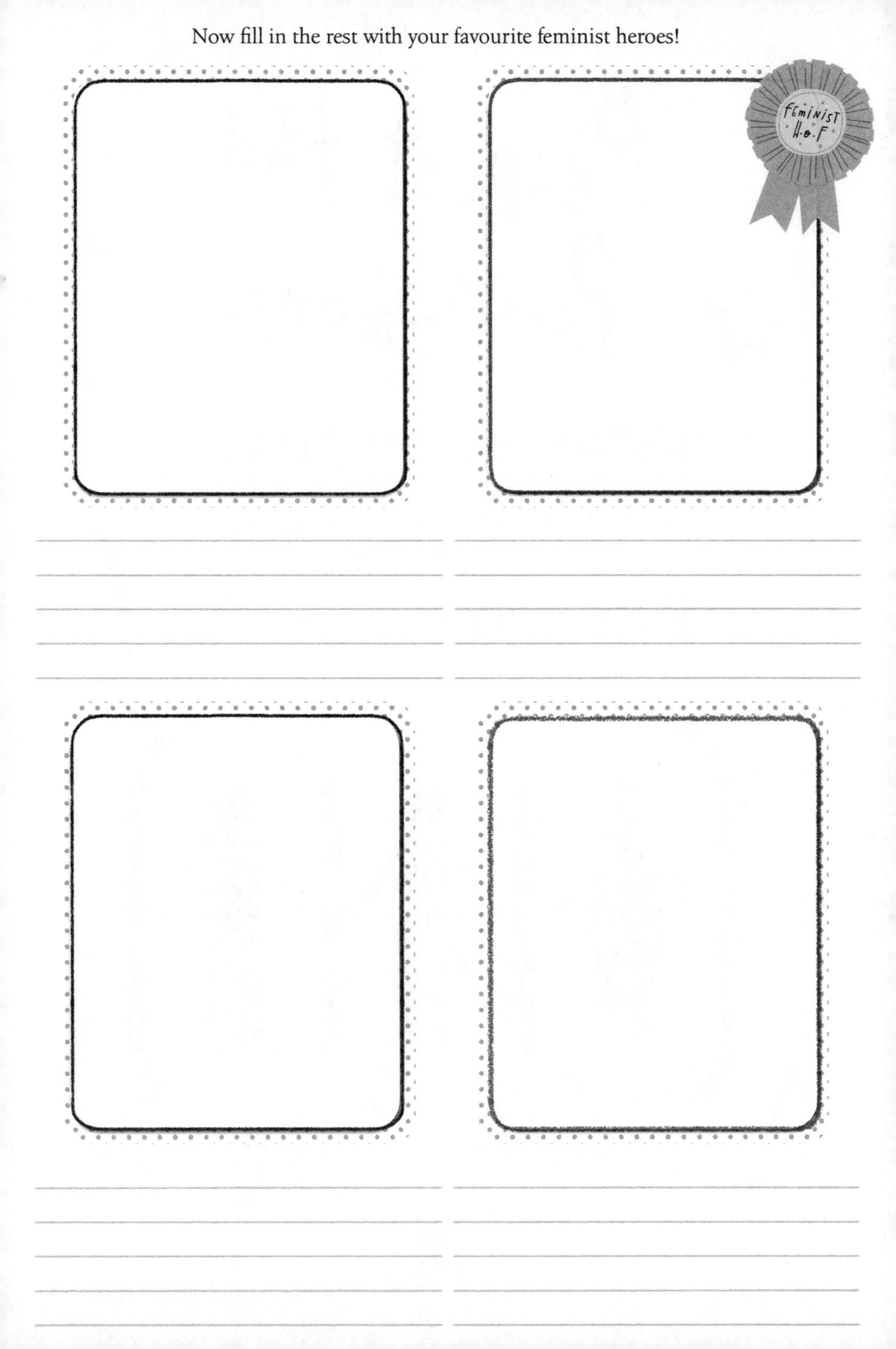

Respect the Pronouns!

REMEMBER to select your pronouns **CAREFULLY** so that you refer to the people around you correctly. This is especially important to keep in mind for non-binary and transgender people.

COLOUR IN and **DECORATE** the pronouns opposite to help you remember!

She/heR
he/hiM
They/TheM

design your own feminist logo

IMAGINE YOU'RE A FEMINIST SUPERHERO–

what would your logo look like?

PLOT TWIST:

You don't actually have to imagine, because you **ARE** your own hero. Now all you need is a logo!

My hope for the future ... in every young girl I meet ... is that they all realize their worth and ask for it.

TAYLOR SWIFT

Colour in and cut out

TAYLOR SWIFT

is an American singer-songwriter and a fearless feminist. One of the bestselling musicians of all time, Swift's songs often explore her personal experiences as a woman. She was the youngest person to be included in *Forbes*' '100 Most Powerful Women' list in 2015.

My hope for the future … in every young girl I meet …
is that they all realize their worth and ask for it.
TAYLOR SWIFT

A SELF-CARE CHECKLIST FOR EVERY FEMINIST

We can spend A LOT of time practicing multi-step skincare routines to get that natural glow. But what if we started implementing multi-step mind care routines to get that mental glow too?

You don't need anything but yourself to get started!

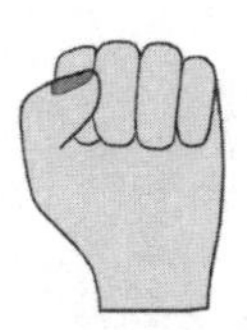

EXFOLIATE your mental space to get rid of all the negative thoughts you've collected today; remind yourself that what people think of you is no reflection of who you are.

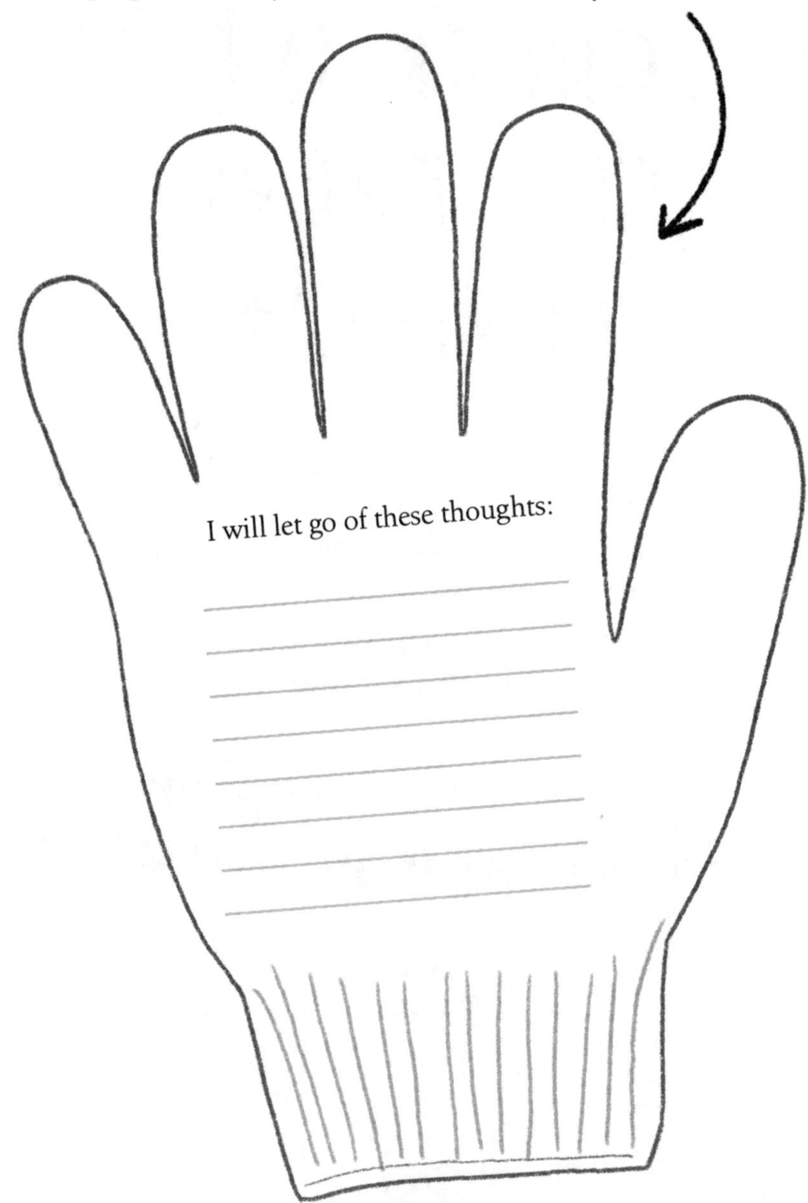
I will let go of these thoughts:

CLEANSE your contact list of all the toxic people who have access to you online by unfollowing and blocking them immediately.

MOISTURIZE your mind with beautiful and inspirational things only – even if that means replaying a voice note from your best friend that says how amazing you are (and if you don't have access to that, record your own voice note to yourself!).

My beautiful things:

TONE down your thoughts with your favourite Spotify playlist and some empowering tunes.

FEMINIST FUEL

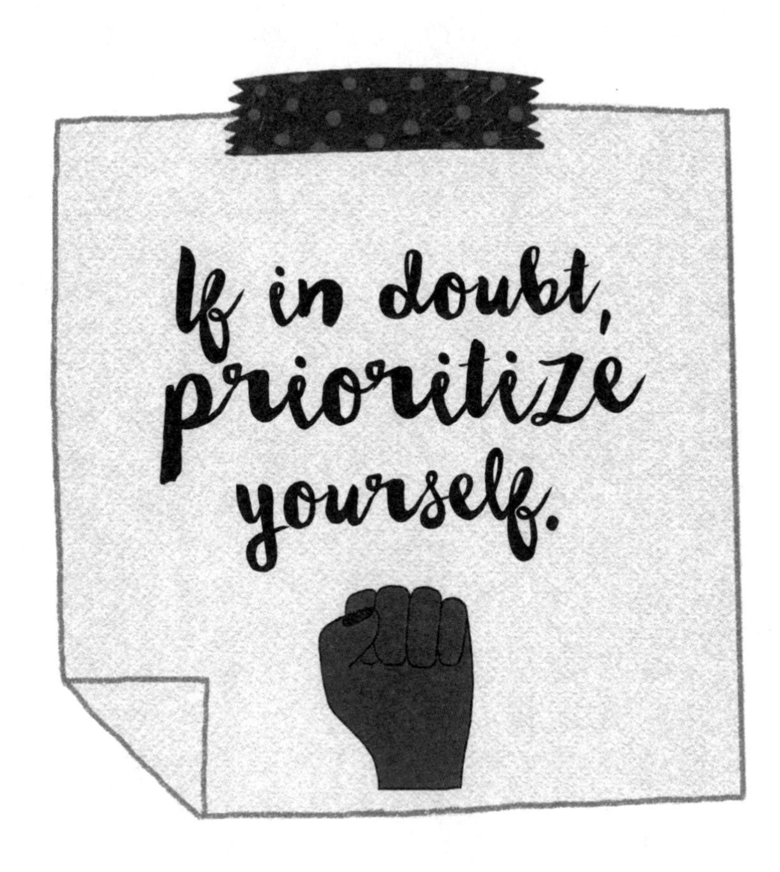
If in doubt, prioritize yourself.

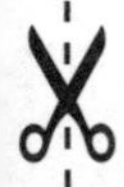

Life presents us with warning signs ALL THE TIME but we don't always pay attention. These warnings often appear in the form of behavioural red flags. Here are some examples.

Colour in each flag you've heard before. If you colour in more than one, it's time for that person to get a copy of SCRIBBLE YOURSELF FEMINIST and begin their own feminist journey. Am I right?!

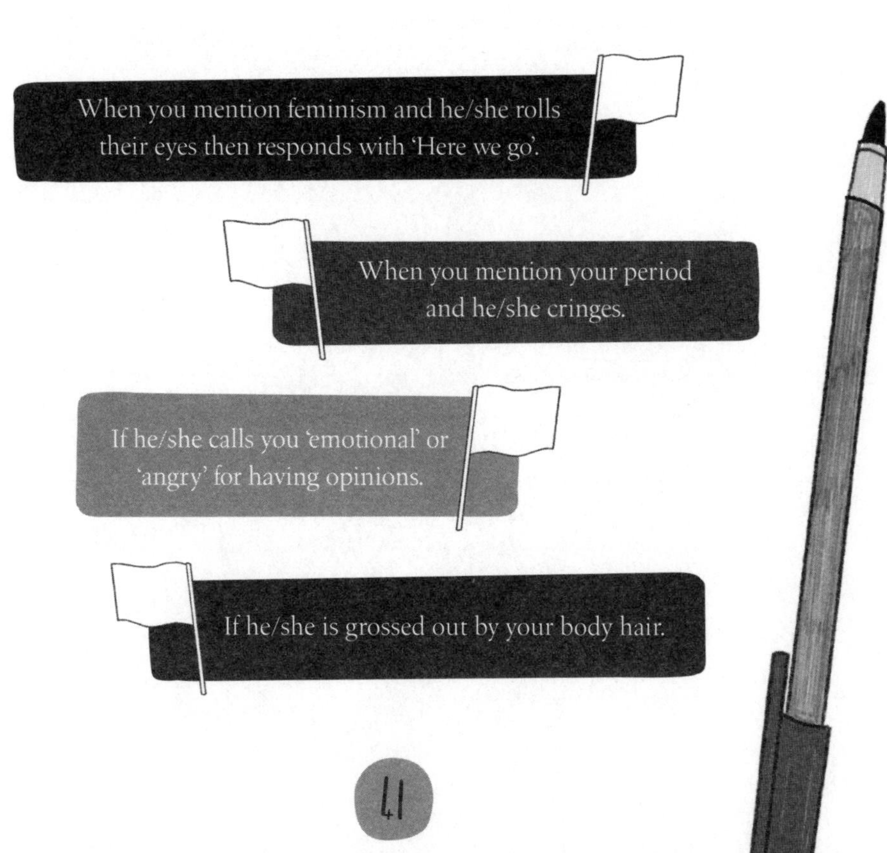

When you mention feminism and he/she rolls their eyes then responds with 'Here we go'.
When you mention your period and he/she cringes.
If he/she calls you 'emotional' or 'angry' for having opinions.
If he/she is grossed out by your body hair.

NOW NOTE DOWN YOUR OWN RED FLAGS AS A REMINDER . . .

When i Grow Up...

CHALLENGING GENDER STEREOTYPES

It's high time we reminded ourselves that, as long as we are equipped with the skillset and determination required to carry out a job, we are **MORE THAN CAPABLE** of doing it! Girls and boys should grow up believing they can be **ANYTHING** they want!

♀♂

Vocational aspirations should not depend on your genitals!

♀♂

Turn the page for some handy visual reminders to **ALWAYS** challenge those stereotypes!

I'm a HAIR-DRESSER and I have a penis
I'm a FLIGHT ATTENDANT and I have a penis
I'm a MIDWIFE and I have a penis
I'm a LIBRARIAN and I have a penis

I'm a
TRUCK driVEr
and I have a VAGINA
I'm a
C.E.O
and I have a
VAGINA
I'm a
FirE
FighTEr
and I
have a
VAGINA
I'm an
EngineEr
and
I'm
NON-
BiNARY

I'm a SURGEON and I have a VAGINA
I'm a CONSTRUCTIO WORKER and I have a VAGINA
I'm a JUDGE and I have a VAGINA
I'm a ASTRONAUT and I have a VAGINA
ASTRONAUT

I'm a FLORIST and I have a penis
I'm a BALLET DANCER and I have a penis
I'm a NURSE and I have a penis
I'm a PERSONAL ASSISTANT and I have a penis

CAN YOU THINK OF
MORE EXAMPLES?

I'M ATTRACTED TO FILMS THAT HAVE strong FEMALE CHARACTERS
BECAUSE THERE ARE strong FEMALE CHARACTERS IN MY LIFE.
ryan gosling

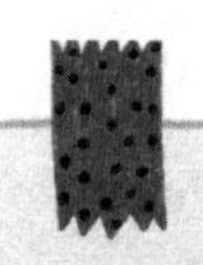

RYAN GOSLING

is a Canadian actor and musician. And the feminist hero of 'Hey, Girl' memes!

FEMINIST FUEL

Rise tall for what your heart believes in, even when your voice shakes.

FEMINIST QUIZ

SO you think you're a feminist? Let's test your knowledge! But guess what? Even if you get some answers wrong, you STILL win because at least you've learned something new!*

1. What year did women get the vote in Switzerland?

A) 1908
B) 1971
C) 1924
D) 1952

2. In 2017, which country granted women the right to drive?

A) MORCOCCO
B) RUSSIA
C) SAUDI ARABIA
D) IRAQ

3. Who sings the lyrics 'Who run the world? GIRLS!'

A) CIARA
B) GWEN STEFANI
C) BEYONCÉ
D) KELLY ROWLAND

*Find the answers at the back of the book!

What stationery product received an enormous online backlash and inspired a very funny sketch by Ellen DeGeneres

A) A PINK CALCULATOR FOR ALL YOUR SHOPPING NEEDS
B) A BIC PEN FOR WOMEN
C) A HEART-PUNCH - A HOLE-PUNCH WITH A TWIST!
D) A STAPLER FOR GIRLS -LIGHTER FOR THOSE FRAGILE HANDS

Which Irish singer-songwriter wrote a letter to Miley "Twerk" Cyrus giving her advice on how to be a woman in the music industry?

A) SINÉAD O'CONNOR
B) ANDREA CORR
C) BONO
D) ENYA

Who was the first woman to win the Nobel Prize for science?

A) ADA LOVELACE
B) CAROLINE HERSCHEL
C) MARY ANNING
D) MARIE CURIE

Who was sentenced to prison for co-publishing a book on birth control?

A) MARIE STOPES
B) LIZZIE BORDEN
C) ANNIE BESANT
D) ANNA LEONOWENS

8. Who performed on stage with victims of sexual assault in 2016?

A) CHER
B) TAYLOR SWIFT
C) LADY GAGA
D) MILEY CYRUS

9. Who was the first US female presidential nominee of a major party?

A) HILLARY CLINTON
B) JACKIE KENNEDY
C) MICHELLE OBAMA
D) IVANKA TRUMP

10. Who was the first woman to travel into space in 1963?

A) MARIE MARVINGT
B) LILIAN BLAND
C) VALENTINA TERESHKOVA
D) JERRIE MOCK

11. Who was the first woman to give birth whilst holding governmental office?

A) MARGARET THATCHER
B) BENAZIR BHUTTO
C) JACINDA ARDERN
D) SIRIMAVO BANDARANAIKE

What was the name of the suffragette who threw herself in front of the King's horse in 1913 to protest for votes for women?

A) EMILY DAVISON
B) EMMELINE PANKHURST
C) FRANCES BALFOUR
D) ANNIE BESANT

What was the name of the movement that arose after the Harvey Weinstein sexual abuse scandal in 2017?

A) #USTOO
B) #SAYNO
C) #METOO
D) #STANDTOGETHER

Who wrote one of the seminal texts of the 1970s feminist movement, entitled *The Female Eunuch*?

A) GERMAINE GREER
B) SIMONE DE BEAUVOIR
C) GLORIA STEINEM
D) FRIDA KAHLO

Which actor is the first female to play the role of Dr Who?

A) EMMA WATSON
B) JODIE WHITTAKER
C) OLIVIA COLEMAN
D) JUDI DENCH

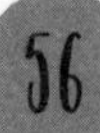

16. Which British sportswoman won the heptathlon gold medal at the London 2012 Olympics, and also became the first British woman to win the BBC Sports Personality of the Year Lifetime Achievement Award in 2017?

A) KELLY HOLMES
B) KATARINA JOHNSON-THOMPSON
C) JESSICA ENNIS-HILL
D) DENISE LEWIS

17. Which tennis player won the Battle of the Sexes tennis match against Bobby Riggs in 1973? Riggs had claimed that a 55-year-old retired professional men's tennis player could beat the current top female players. Her victory was significant in gaining greater respect for the women's game.

A) SERENA WILLIAMS
B) MARTINA NAVRATILOVA
C) CHRIS EVERT
D) BILLIE JEAN KING

18. Who started the Everyday Sexism Project in 2012, a website documenting examples of everyday sexism from across the world?

A) NATALIE PORTMAN
B) EMMA WATSON
C) LAURA BATES
D) MALALA YOUSAFZAI

Who wrote the 1982 novel *The Color Purple*? It documents a young black woman's fight against both racism and sexism in 1930s America.

A) OPRAH WINFREY
B) ALICE WALKER
C) ZADIE SMITH
D) ALICE DUNBAR-NELSON

Who wrote the book *How To Be a Woman* in 2011?

A) LENA DUNHAM
B) ZOE WILLIAMS
C) HADLEY FREEMAN
D) CAITLIN MORAN

Which Tudor Queen ruled England for 44 years from 1558-1603?

A) MARY I
B) ELIZABETH I
C) MARY, QUEEN OF SCOTS
D) ANNE BOLEYN

Who was the first woman to be awarded the Nobel Prize for Literature in 1909?

A) SELMA LAGERLÖF
B) NELLY SACHS
C) TONI MORRISON
D) ALICE MUNRO

NO COUNTRY CAN FLOURISH IF IT STIFLES THE POTENTIAL OF ITS WOMEN AND DEPRIVES ITSELF OF THE CONTRIBUTIONS OF HALF OF ITS CITIZENS

MICHELLE OBAMA

MICHELLE OBAMA

is an American lawyer, writer and former First Lady of the United States (the first African-American to hold this position). During her time as First Lady, she became known around the world as a fierce promoter of women's and LGBT rights. She also led campaigns to tackle obesity and homelessness and, in 2015, launched Let Girls Learn, a US government initiative to help teenage girls attend and stay in school.

NO COUNTRY CAN FLOURISH IF IT STIFLES THE POTENTIAL OF ITS WOMEN AND DEPRIVES ITSELF OF THE CONTRIBUTIONS OF HALF OF ITS CITIZENS
MICHELLE OBAMA

DESIGN YOUR OWN FEMINIST WARDROBE

Fashion is more than just about serving looks. Fashion is a STATEMENT of how you feel about yourself. Our clothes don't just cover our bodies; our clothes can reveal our beliefs and IDENTITY.

Do you ever leave your house in a particular outfit and feel like you're embodying a character? A mood? An EMOTION? If the answer's yes, then you'll love this activity.

Use these slogans, and come up with some of your own, to decorate these wardrobe essentials.

* SPEND LESS TIME ON HIM AND MORE TIME ON YOUR SKINCARE, HONEY!
* FOCUS ON WORLD DOMINATION, BABY!
* GENDER FLUID AND PROUD!

UNLEASH
your inner
feminist
fashionista!

Write your own ACROSTIC

Sometimes, you've gotta spell it out for it to sink in. GO ON, give it a go and see what you come up with . . .

Here's one I prepared earlier, for a little inspo:

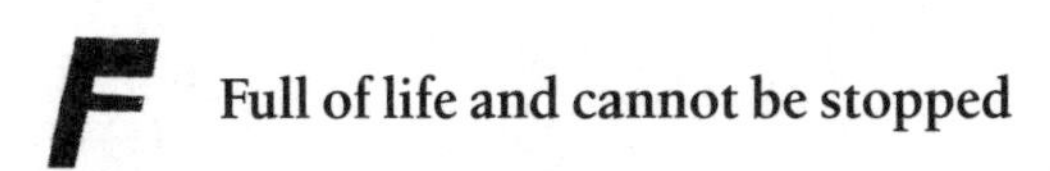

F Full of life and cannot be stopped

E Everything about me is incredible

M Magic should be my middle name cos that's all I create!

I Imagination is my superpower

N Nothing can stop me unless I give it permission to

I Intelligence comes natural to me

S Stop what you're doing and tell yourself how awesome you are, cos . . .

T Tomorrow might not come! So act now!

NOW IT'S YOUR TURN:

V

A

G

I

N

A

BEYONCÉ

V

O

T

E

S

NOW SHARE IT ONLINE AND KEEP THE CONVERSATION GOING.

FEMINIST FUEL

Remember that
a boss is simply
someone who believes
in their value.

which feminist hero are you? ♀♂

FEMINIST HEROES WALK AMONG US!

Some are performers and artists, some are politicians and writers. But what do they all have in common? The POWER to change the world by recognizing that we can all individually do BETTER!

Here's a fun chart to help you find the feminist hero that's most like you. When I did the quiz, GUESS WHO I GOT? Oprah! I've had loads of people tell me I remind them of Oprah through my ability to connect with women so I'm THRILLED with the result. You should totally give this a go; you never know, you might even be shocked!

Don't forget to compare results with your mates and totally share your results on your social feeds – remember,

the revolution begins with you.

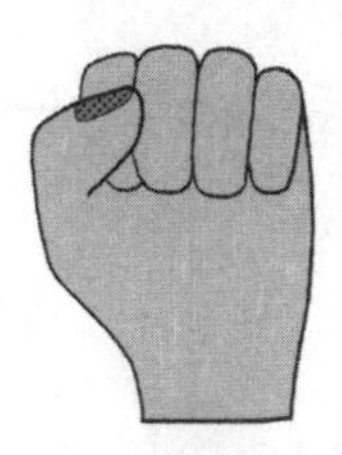

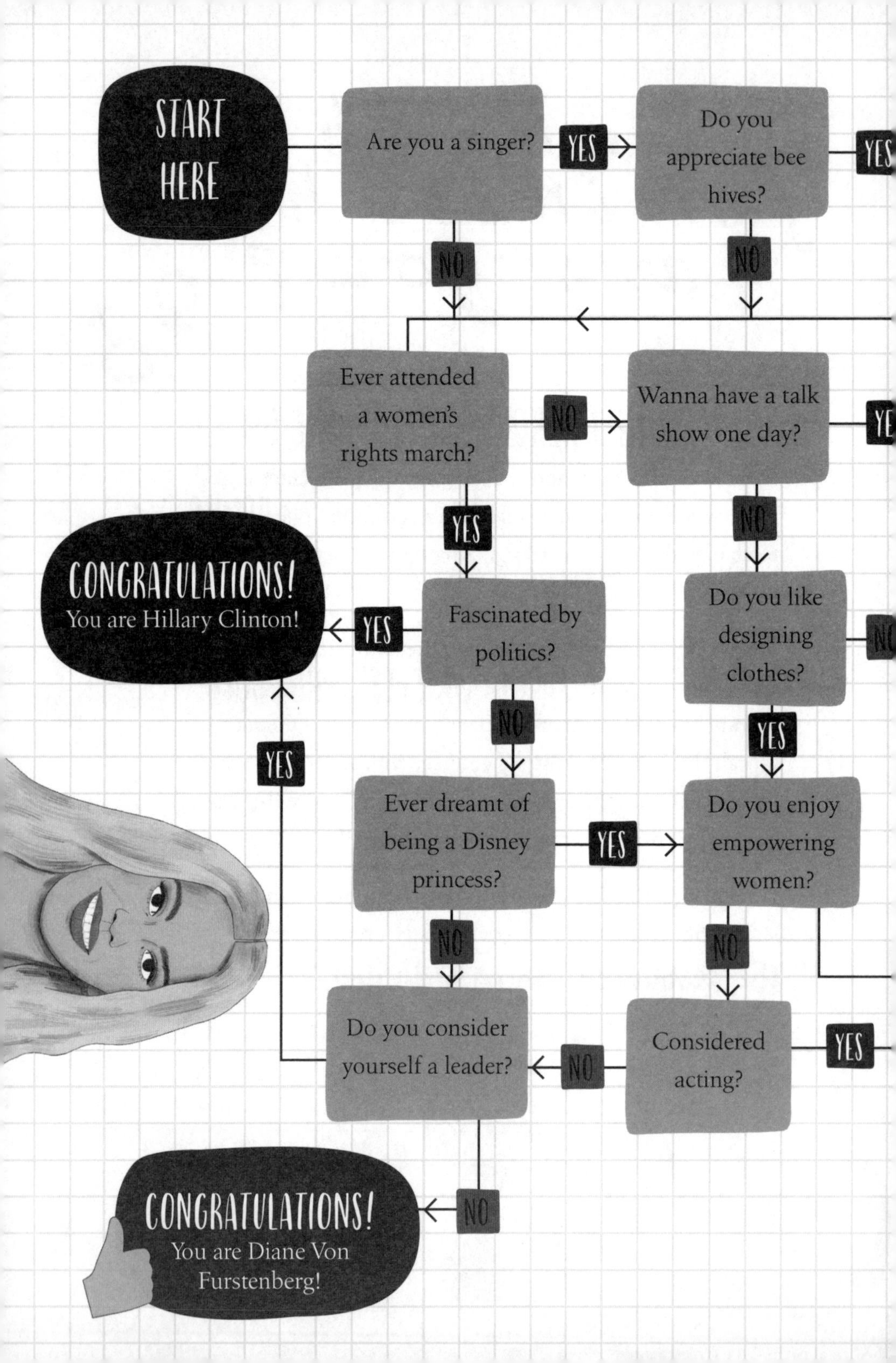
START HERE
Are you a singer?
YES
Do you appreciate bee hives?
YES
NO
NO
Ever attended a women's rights march?
NO
Wanna have a talk show one day?
YES
NO
Fascinated by politics?
YES
CONGRATULATIONS! You are Hillary Clinton!
Do you like designing clothes?
YES
NO
Ever dreamt of being a Disney princess?
YES
Do you enjoy empowering women?
NO
NO
YES
Do you consider yourself a leader?
NO
Considered acting?
YES
NO
CONGRATULATIONS! You are Diane Von Furstenberg!

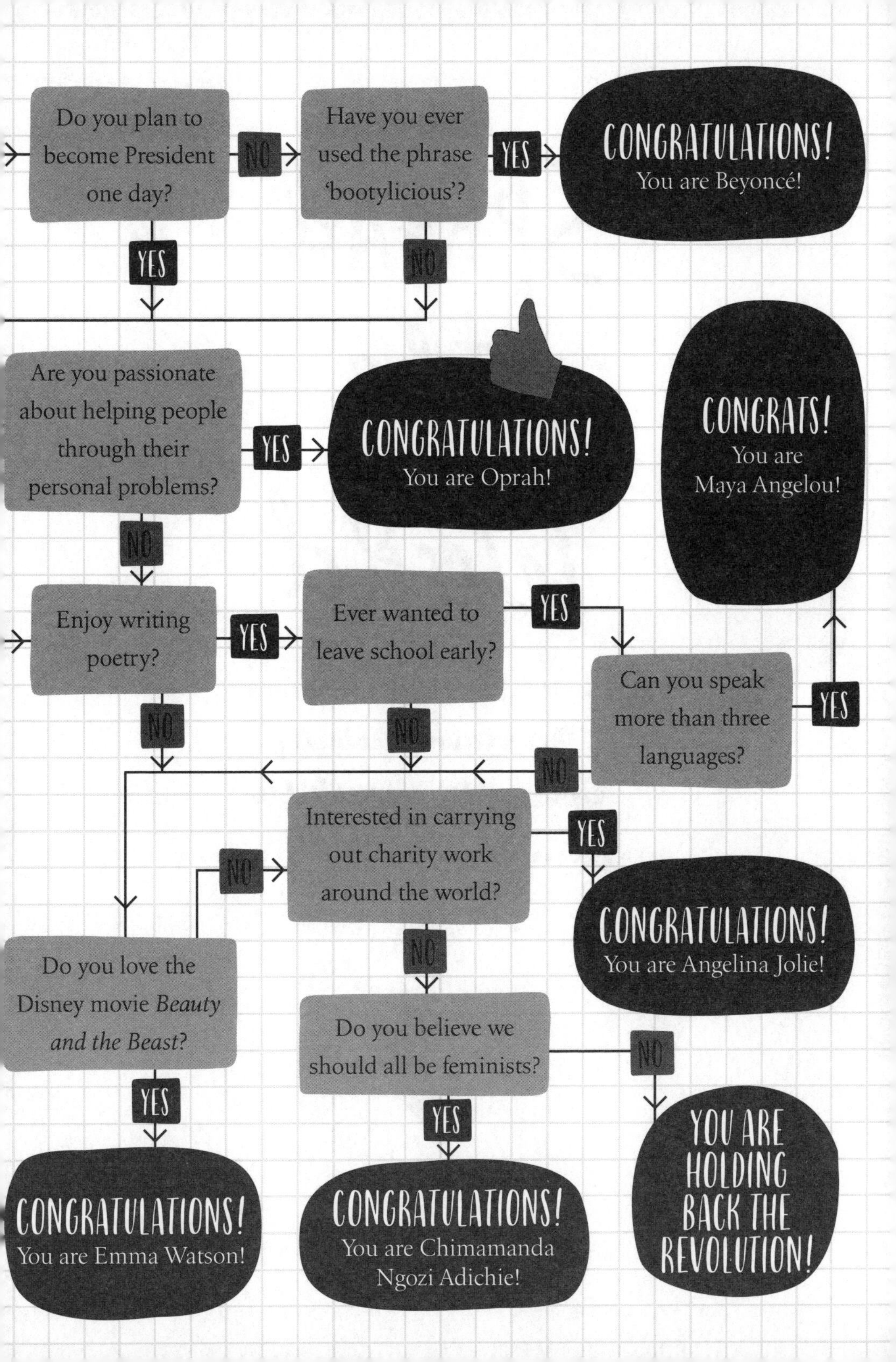

Do you plan to become President one day?
NO
YES
Have you ever used the phrase 'bootylicious'?
YES
NO
CONGRATULATIONS! You are Beyoncé!
Are you passionate about helping people through their personal problems?
YES
NO
CONGRATULATIONS! You are Oprah!
CONGRATS! You are Maya Angelou!
Enjoy writing poetry?
YES
NO
Ever wanted to leave school early?
YES
NO
Can you speak more than three languages?
YES
NO
Interested in carrying out charity work around the world?
YES
NO
CONGRATULATIONS! You are Angelina Jolie!
Do you love the Disney movie *Beauty and the Beast*?
NO
YES
Do you believe we should all be feminists?
NO
YES
CONGRATULATIONS! You are Emma Watson!
CONGRATULATIONS! You are Chimamanda Ngozi Adichie!
YOU ARE HOLDING BACK THE REVOLUTION!

Spread the Word

Life is hard but your spirit is stronger.

You are undefeatable; unstoppable; unbreakable.

But maybe you know people who need a bit of help to feel unstoppable? Who do YOU want to send an empowering message to?

Today, I am motivated to . . .

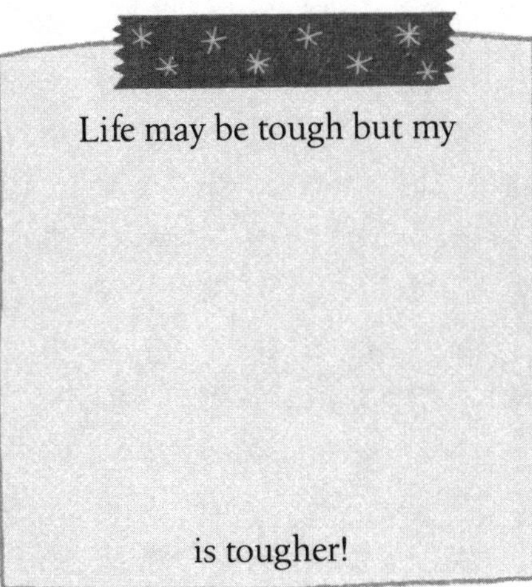
Life may be tough but my
is tougher!

Hey, I know Donald Trump is President but
look on the bright side: at least you . . .

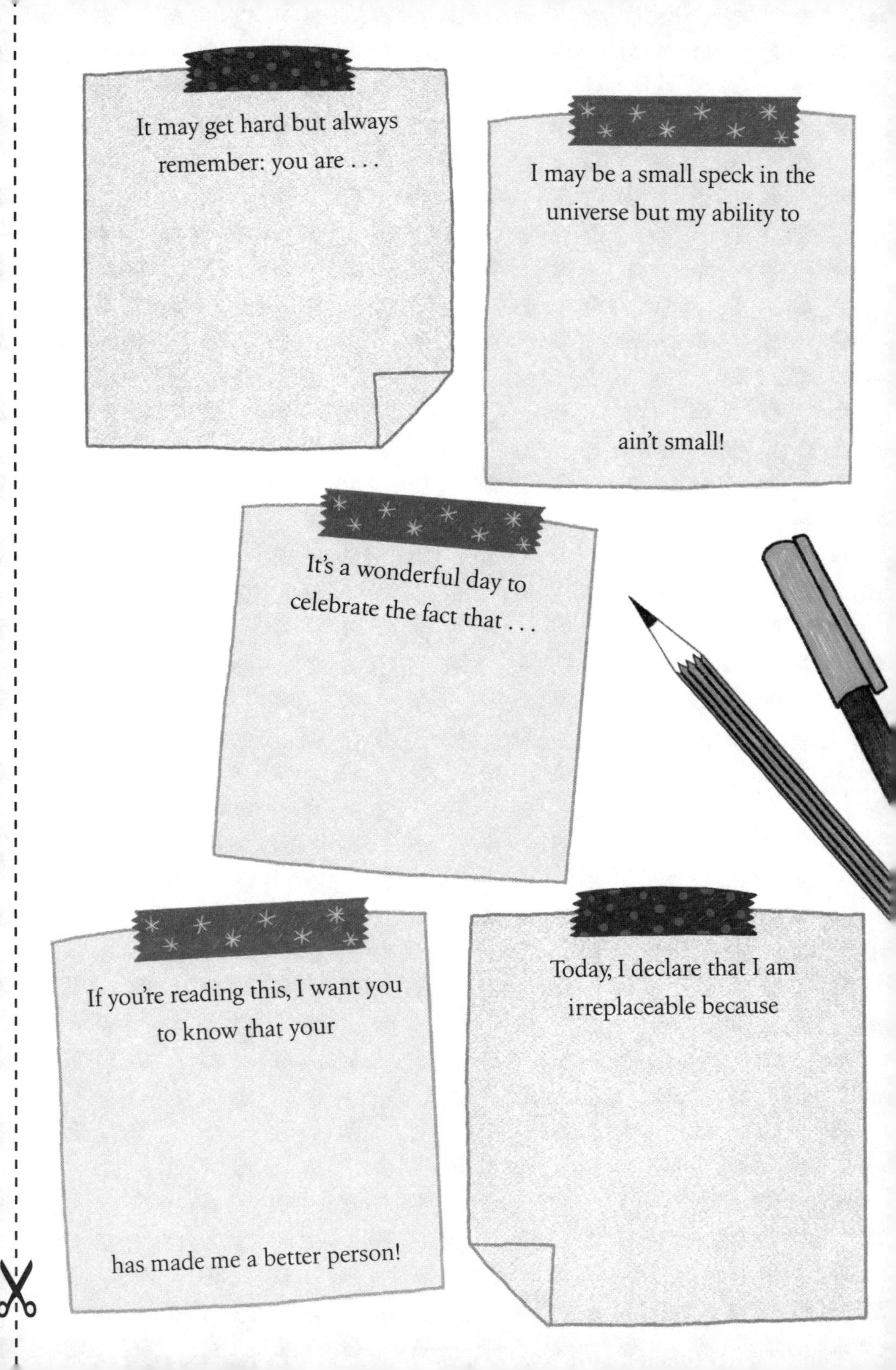
It may get hard but always remember: you are . . .
I may be a small speck in the universe but my ability to
ain't small!
It's a wonderful day to celebrate the fact that . . .
If you're reading this, I want you to know that your
has made me a better person!
Today, I declare that I am irreplaceable because

YOU DESERVE
THE BEST,
THE VERY
BEST
BECAUSE
YOU ARE
ONE OF
THE FEW
PEOPLE
IN THIS
LOUSY
WORLD
WHO ARE
HONEST
TO
THEMSELVES,
AND
THAT IS
THE
ONLY
THING
THAT
MATTERS.
fridA
Kahlo

FRIDA KAHLO

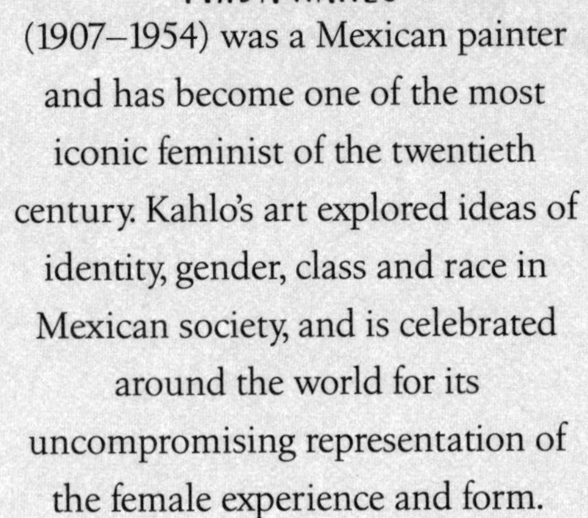

(1907–1954) was a Mexican painter and has become one of the most iconic feminist of the twentieth century. Kahlo's art explored ideas of identity, gender, class and race in Mexican society, and is celebrated around the world for its uncompromising representation of the female experience and form.

YOU DESERVE THE BEST, THE VERY BEST BECAUSE YOU ARE ONE OF THE FEW PEOPLE IN THIS LOUSY WORLD
WHO ARE HONEST TO THEMSELVES, AND THAT IS THE ONLY THING THAT MATTERS.
fridA Kahlo

deck out your bedroom, feminist style

♀ ♂

Your bedroom is more than just four walls. Your bedroom is a SELF-LOVE SANCTUARY. A haven. A hideout! It's a space that can really reflect who you are.

My bedroom is a total mess most of the time but it's my FAVOURITE place in the world to spend time with myself.

Imagine if you could create your IDEAL BEDROOM. What would it look like? What bold statements would you make in YOUR safe space?

Did someone say Fem Shui . . . ?

Reconnect With Your Vagina

GIRL, YOUR VAGINA IS SACRED!

Here's a space to celebrate your vagina with these epic mandala* colouring designs.

*The Tibetan mandala, a tool for gaining wisdom and compassion, is often depicted as an intricate, geometric pattern wherein deities reside . . .

I HAVE THE HEART AND THE STOMACH OF A KING.

ELIZABETH I

ELIZABETH I

(1533–1603) is often considered to be one of the greatest monarchs in English history. She became Queen of England and Ireland when she was twenty-five, inheriting a bankrupt and deeply unstable country. Although Elizabeth was expected to marry and produce an heir, she never did. She ruled alone until her death, nearly half a century later, by which time she had turned her country into one of the leading nations of the day.

I HAVE THE HEART AND THE STOMACH OF A KING.
ELIZABETH I

EMERGENCY FEMINIST KIT!

This is for those moments when your witty comeback hasn't come to you in time and you need to have a quick dose of **EMERGENCY POSITIVE FEMINISM** so you don't lose your faith in the world! Tapping out is never a bad idea.

SELF-CARE COMES FIRST!

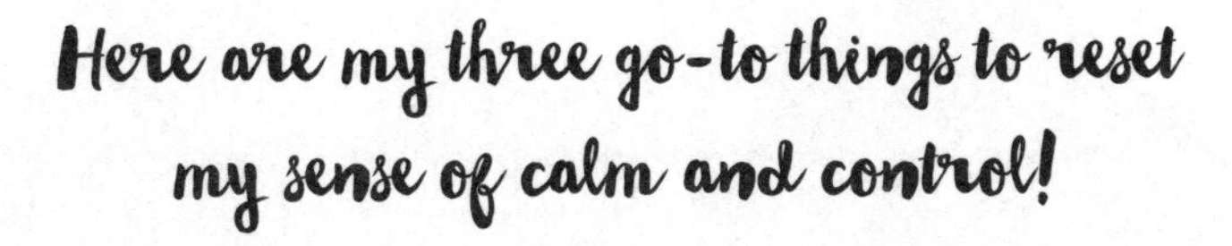

Here are my three go-to things to reset my sense of calm and control!

1.

If in doubt, call up a Ryan Gosling feminist meme!
Now, we all know Ryan Gosling is an absolute babe of life and his role in *The Notebook* was the start of our group romance with him. So when you're feeling down and drained, remember this meme:

HEY GIRL.
WHEN YOU TALK I HEAR THE REVOLUTIONS.

Or if the Ryans of this world are not your bag, you could turn to another **BABE**, like Gal Gadot – Wonder Woman herself.

I WANTED TO SHOW THAT WOMEN ARE EMPOWERED AND STRONG, AND DON'T HAVE TO BE SAVED BY SOME MALE HERO, BUT THEY CAN TAKE CARE OF THEMSELVES USING THEIR INTELLIGENCE AND POWER.

Turn on Beyoncé's 'Run the World' and let Queen Bey's awesomeness calm your storm!

I mean, c'mon! Beyonce is the mother of SLAY. Plus, it's important to remind yourself that girls run the world when you're running low on feminist juice!

Open a copy of Caitlin Moran's ***How To Be a Woman***

A little reminder ain't gonna hurt nobody, right? This book answers all the questions. Yes, all of them. From Botox and Brazilian butt jobs, to whether it's true that men hate us, this book has got your back!

What would **YOUR** emergency feminist first aid kit have in it?

FEMINIST FUEL

Never let anybody speak over you.

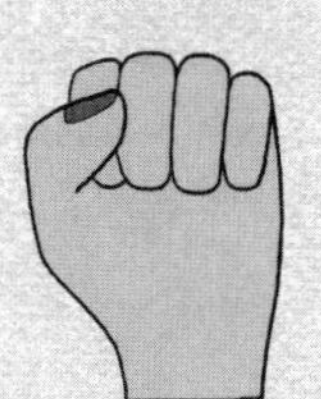

BECAUSE EVEN CATS KNOW WHEN TO SAY ENOUGH IS ENOUGH!

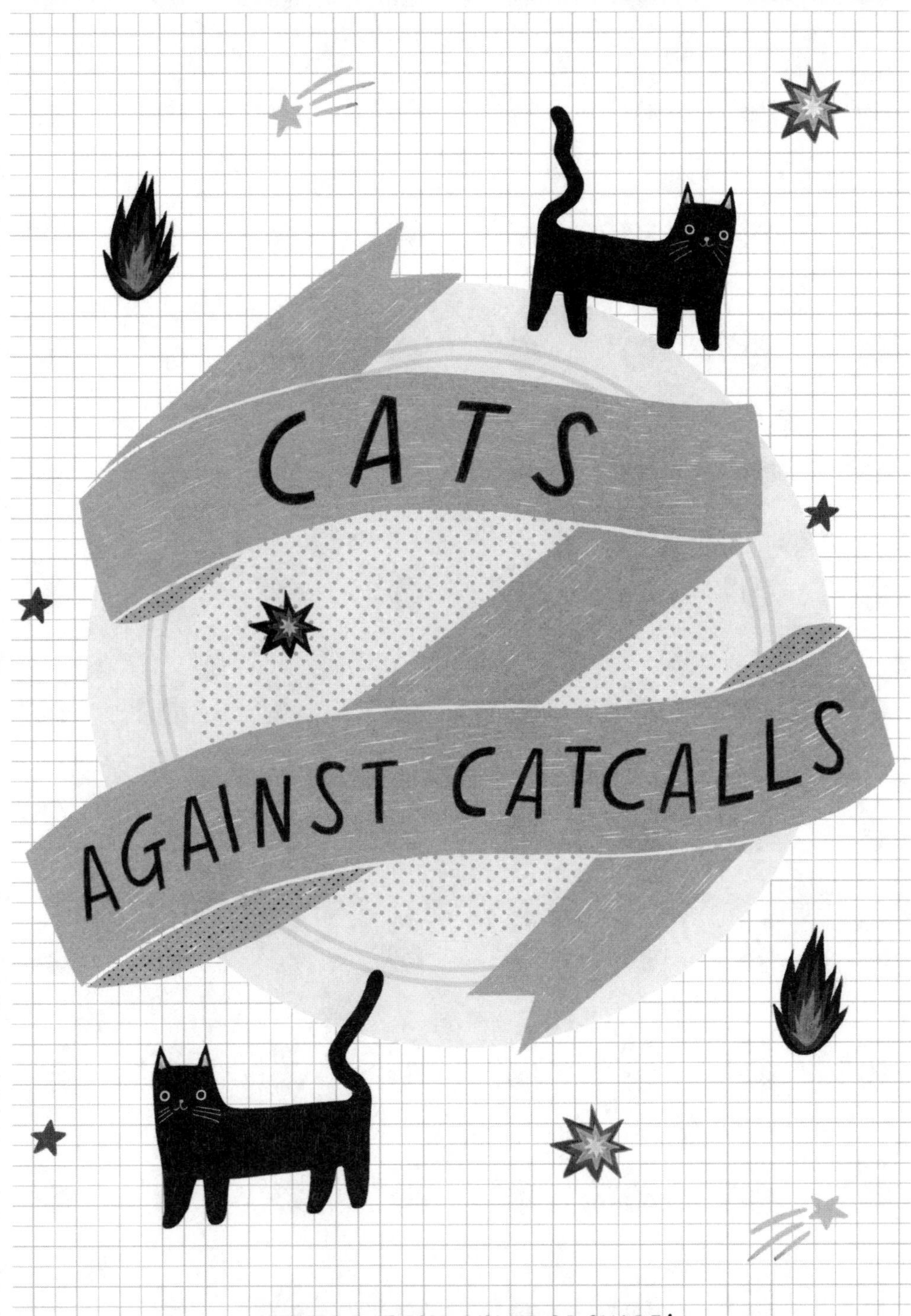

CUT ME OUT AND PIN UP OR SHARE!

EVERYONE IS A complicated HUMAN BEING, AND

EVERYONE IS strong AND weak AND funny AND scared.

LAVERNE COX

LAVERNE COX

is an American actress and LGBT activist. In 2014 she became the first openly transgender person to be nominated for an Emmy Award for her role as Sophia Burset in the TV series *Orange Is the New Black*. That same year, she became the first openly transgender person to appear on the cover of *Time* magazine.

FEMINIST FUEL

You are as strong as you allow yourself to believe.

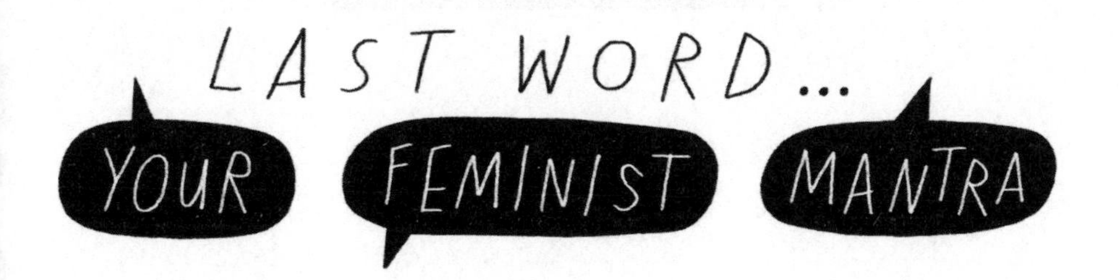

Now have a go at writing your very own mantra to carry you on your **FEMINIST JOURNEY!**

Here's mine:

I am bossy. I am talented. I am great. Anything I set my hands on will prosper and flourish!

YOUR TURN!

Now, when you're having a bad day, repeat this to yourself in the mirror. **YOU'VE GOT THIS, GIRL!**

CONGRATULATIONS!

YOU ARE NOW A NOTABLE FEMINIST.

Thank you for helping to create a
HAPPIER AND SAFER
world for the benefit of all!

Turn the page to collect your certificate . . .

THIS CERTIFICAT

____

for

WOMEN

IS AWARDED TO:

____

being a

OF NOTE

'i believe the rights of women and girls is the unfinished business of the 21st century'

-Hillary Clinton

A girl should be two things: classy and fabulous
COCO CHANEL

GABRIELLE BONHEUR 'COCO' CHANEL

(1883–1971) was one of the most iconic fashion designers of the twentieth century. Born into poverty, Chanel made her living as a seamstress and hat designer before establishing her now world-famous brand in 1910. Her innovative designs redefined women's fashion in the 1920s – she made it normal for women to wear trousers! – and many of her styles, such as the little black dress, remain unchanged to this day.

A girl should be two things: classy and fabulous
COCO CHANEL

Now that you've completed all of our awesome activities, this is your space to **WRITE, DOODLE, SHAPE** or **DRAW** whatever you like!

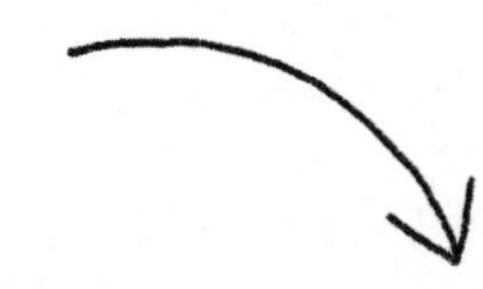

FEMINIST QUIZ

THE ANSWERS

1. B
2. C
3. C
4. B
5. A
6. D
7. C
8. C
9. A
10. C
11. B
12. A
13. C
14. A
15. B
16. C
17. D
18. C
19. B
20. D
21. B
22. A